TARANGINI

1

Swami Chinmayananda

and

Swamini Saradapriyananda

CENTRAL CHINMAYA MISSION TRUST
MUMBAI - 400 072

Printed between	1991 -	2005 -	26,000 copies
Revised Edition	Dec. -	2008 -	3,000 copies

Published by:
CENTRAL CHINMAYA MISSION TRUST
Sandeepany Sadhanalaya,
Saki Vihar Road,
Mumbai - 400 072, INDIA.
Tel: (+91-22) 2857 2367 / 2857 5806
Fax: (+91-22) 2857 3065
Email: ccmt@chinmayamission.com
Website: www.chinmayamission.com

Distribution Centre in USA:
CHINMAYA MISSION WEST
Publications Division,
560 Bridgetown Pike,
Langhorne, PA 19053, USA.
Tel: (215) 396-0390
Fax: (215) 396-9710
Email: publications@chinmaya.org
Website: www.chinmayapublications.org

Design and Illustrations:
Nina Bahl

Printed by:
JAK Printers Pvt Ltd.,
Mumbai.

Price: Rs. 130.00

ISBN : 978-81-7597-443-2

CONTENTS

1. Lord Ganesha 5
2. Only One Fruit 10
3. The Granny with the Fire and the Cock 13
4. The Saving Name 17
5. The Foolish Tapas 20
6. Chattambi Swamigal 26
7. The Heart in the Tree 30
8. The Silly Fly 41
9. The Ant and the Baby 46
10. Ambarisha 50
11. Gajendra Moksha 57
12. The Truthful Cow 62
13. Kannappa 67
14. Action Songs (Four)
    1. Honey Bee 74
    2. Roses 75
    3. The Cat in Kailash 76
    4. Hari Om 77
15. Dhruva (A One-Act Play) 78
16. Sweetness 94
17. Code of Conduct for Chinmaya Mission Members 95
18. The Chinmaya Mission Pledge 96

Listen!
Ye Children
of
Immortal Bliss!

Lord Ganesha

One day, Parvati, the wife of Lord Shiva, was going for her bath. As she waited for hot water, she mixed some gram flour for her bath. Then, she fashioned the figure of a small boy from the flour. Parvati thought it would be a pity to use the flour for her bath and destroy the figure. An idea came to her — Why not give it life? She brought it to life and was thrilled beyond words when the boy called out, "Mother." Beaming with joy, Parvati embraced the boy and said,"My darling, I love you! From now on you will be my son!"

Smiling, the boy said, "Yes, Mother, what do you wish me to do?" Parvati smiled happily

and said, "Son, I am going for my bath now. Keep watch at the door and do not allow anyone to come in."

The boy stood at the door while Parvati bathed inside. During that time Lord Shiva came unexpectedly and was about to enter the house. Unaware that the Lord was his own mother's husband, the boy barred his way and said, "No Sir, you cannot go in. Mother is bathing."

Shiva was surprised. He looked at the little fellow who blocked his way. Where had this

boy come from? And why did he call Parvati 'Mother'? Shiva and Parvati had no children. So he brushed the boy aside and tried to move in. But the boy was very firm. He came back, stood in the middle of the doorway and stretched his little hands across, obstructing the Lord. "I told you, you cannot go in," he shouted. "I will punish you if you disobey."

Shiva could not believe being stopped from entering his own house. In a fit of rage, he chopped off the boy's head and went in. Parvati had just finished her bath and was combing her hair. Seeing Shiva, she smiled and said, "How did you come in? Didn't my son stop you?" Shiva was stunned. "Your son? Then, what the boy said was true. I did not believe him when he claimed to be your son." "Yes," Parvati said proudly, "He is my own darling son. Is he not cute? I made him with gram flour and infused life into him." A sudden thought hit her. "If my son was there, how did you get in? Did he not stop you?"

Shiva's heart was heavy with remorse. He said in a low voice, "I am sorry. I did not know

any of this. When the boy came in my way, I thought that he was some impudent fellow. So I cut off his head and came in."

Parvati was horrified. "Oh, how cruel you are! You have killed my beautiful darling son. You have no love for me." And she wept inconsolably for her son. Shiva could not bear to see tears in the eyes of his beloved wife. He quickly went out to see whether the boy could be brought back to life. Alas! He found only the body lying in a pool of blood. The head was nowhere to be seen. What was the use of giving life to the trunk alone? Shiva sent his attendants everywhere to look for the missing head. But in vain. He thought hard and sent his attendants out again. "Go and search for any living being who is asleep, with its head towards the north, be it human, animal or bird. Cut off its head and bring it to me."

The attendants searched everywhere but found no being. Just when they were about to give up, they found an elephant sleeping with its head towards the north. They immediately chopped off its head and brought it to Shiva.

The Lord joined the elephant's head to the trunk of the body and infused him with life. The boy woke up as if from sleep and cried out, 'Mother!' Parvati was very happy and embraced him with great joy.

Thus the boy came to be elephant-headed and was named Gajanana. Lord Shiva made him the leader of all his attendants. So he is also known as Ganapati. Ganapati is the Lord of all obstacles. If he is pleased, he removes all obstacles and makes sure that our work is successful. That is why people also call him Vighneshwara and pray to him before beginning any new task.

शुक्लांबरधरं विष्णुं शशिवर्णं चतुर्भुजम्।
प्रसन्नवदनं ध्यायेत् सर्वविघ्नोपशान्तये।।

shuklambaradharam vishnum shashivarnam chaturbhujam
prasannavadanam dhyayet sarva vighnopashantaye

(For the removal of obstacles, meditate on Him, pleasant and brilliant, four-handed, all pervading, and clothed in white!)

Only One Fruit

Once upon a time there lived a woman who had no children. She approached a great sage and begged him for the boon of a child. The sage took pity on her and told her to go to a mango tree close by, pluck one ripe fruit and eat it. Then she would give birth to a son. The grateful woman prostrated before him and went to the tree to get a mango.

When she looked up at the tree, she saw hundreds of ripe mangoes hanging in big bunches from its branches. Her mouth watered as she thought, "The sage said that if I ate one fruit I would get one child. But there are so many mangoes here! He would hardly notice my taking one or two extra mangoes."

Slowly she climbed the tree and plucked four or five fruits. But by the time she came down she was surprised to find only one fruit in her hand. Where had the other mangoes gone? Had they fallen from her hands when she was coming down? She searched everywhere but could not find them. So she went up the tree once more and plucked five more fruits. This

time she carefully bundled them in one corner of her saree, and took care to see that not a single fruit fell out of the bundle. But when she opened her pallu after reaching the ground, she found only one fruit. How and where had the mangoes disappeared? She was confused.

The woman climbed the tree a third time. This time she plucked ten mangoes and tied them firmly to her pallu. Then she came down. Again the same mystery. Of the ten, only one fruit remained tied in her pallu. She looked up at the tree and was amazed to see the nine that she had plucked back hanging on the tree as before.

It was then that the truth dawned upon her. She realised that the sage had granted only one fruit to her and that she should not try to get any more. One fruit and therefore only one son was all that she could have. She learnt to be satisfied with her lot and to stop craving for more.

The Granny with the Fire and the Cock

An old granny lived in a small village where everybody knew everybody else. She had a cock that crowed early every morning before sunrise. The crowing of the cock could be heard in every corner of the village, and the villagers woke up on hearing its sound.

Being very old, the granny did not sleep long. She woke up every day long before the cock crowed and lit her oven. By the time the villagers finished their morning ablutions and were ready to light their fires, the granny's fire would be blazing away. All of them knew this, so they came to her and she gladly let them light their fires from hers. Often, they would praise her and say, "Granny, what would we do without your fire and the cock's crow!"

Hearing such praise from the villagers repeatedly, the seeds of pride began to grow within the old lady. She came to believe that the villagers could not live without her. "Really speaking, they should honour and respect me for all that I do for them. But they take me for granted." The more she thought about it, the more she was convinced of her importance to the villagers. And the old granny began to feel that she should be treated like a V.I.P. She thought, "One day I will make them realize the importance of the fire and the cock."

So, one fine morning she packed her things and left the village along with her cock and her fire. She reached a nearby forest and began

living on its farthest side."Wait and see. Now they will miss me and come searching for me," she thought.

And so she lived, dreaming of the day when all the villagers would come to find her and tearfully plead with her to return to the village. She imagined how she would pretend not to be interested in returning. Then she would reluctantly consent to return to the village, for their sake. But a week passed, then two, then a month, six months... but there was no sign of anyone. Not a soul came to search for her, let alone beg her to return.

What had happened in the village after she left? She was very anxious to know, but there was no one whom she could ask. At last, one day she saw a man from the village walking on the road bordering the forest. Unable to contain herself, she ran after him, waving her hand and calling out to him loudly. He heard her calling and stopped. The old granny asked, "Are you not from the village near the river?" "Yes," the man replied. "Do you know anyone in our village?"

The granny's heart sank when she saw that he had not even recognized her. In a low voice she enquired, "Are the villagers getting up in the morning? Are they cooking their food?"

The man stared hard at her. What a strange question! Was she mad? Could there be a village where people did not get up in the morning? Could there be a house where there was no cooking?

He nodded his head and said, "Of course. All of us get up in the morning and all of us cook our food." Not wanting to waste his time talking to the silly old woman, he went on his way.

Poor granny! How disappointed she was! Nobody had missed her. The villagers had carried on with their lives without her cock and even her fire. Nobody would ever send for her. Sadly, she packed her things and returned to the village. But her pride had made her stay away too long. Now no one came to her for fire or waited for her cock to crow.

The Saving Name

In a certain village there lived a great Pundit who earned his living by explaining the Ramayana to the people. Every day he would go to a different place to give discourses, for which he had to start very early from home. He would drink a glass of milk before he left his house. But the milkmaid was always late and delayed him. One day he asked her why she could not come a little earlier. She replied that her house was on the other side of the river and that she had to cross it by ferry. The boatman came late and so she was late. Hearing this, the Pundit loftily quoted from the Ramayana, "Rama Nama takes one across the ocean of Samsara. Why can you not cross a small river by taking Rama's name?"

The milkmaid listened to the wise words of the Pundit. Simple and illiterate, she had absolute faith in the truth of the Pundit's words. From the very next day she did not wait for the ferry. As soon as the cow was milked, she took the milk in a pot, placed it on her head and came to the river. With complete faith she would utter

Rama Nama and walk on the water to cross the river. In this way, not only did she supply the milk in time but she also saved some money. She felt very grateful to the Pundit. One day, she invited him to sanctify her house by his presence.

He agreed to her request and came to the river. The milkmaid walked on the waters uttering the sacred name while the Pundit stood helplessly on the banks, waiting for the ferry. The milkmaid turned back to see how far the Pundit had come, and was surprised to find him still standing on the other bank. She said, "Sir, I believed in what you said and crossed the river with the help of the Lord's name. But you, who daily preach the greatness of the name to all, why are you not able to walk over this small river?" At these words of the milkmaid, the Pundit felt ashamed at his lack of faith.

The Foolish Tapas

In a certain village there lived two men, Raman and Sankaran, who were neighbours. There were petty jealousies and quarrels between them and each vied to get the best of the other. Gradually their mutual dislike reached a point where neither could tolerate the thought of the other being happy or prosperous.

One day Raman thought hard and long as to how he could outdo his rival. He decided that he had better do tapas and get boons from the Lord so that he could be one up on Sankaran. Like minds think alike. At that very moment, the same idea crossed the mind of Sankaran. He told his wife that he would go to the temple early next morning to sit in prayer until the Lord gave him darshan. Raman also decided upon the same thing.

The next day, by the time Raman reached the temple, he could hear the voice of Sankaran from one side of the temple, loudly chanting, "Om Namah Shivaya". Raman ground his teeth in rage. His rival too wanted to get boons from the Lord! He would see who would succeed! He noticed that Sankaran was sitting under a tree on the right side of the temple. So he sat under another tree on the left side of the temple. He

did not want to take up the same mantra. So he chanted, “Sivaya Namah Om”. Sankaran pricked up his ears when he heard Raman’s voice. That fellow here too! All right! He would see who fared better!

The two rivals sat, day in and day out, not budging an inch from their places. Each was afraid that if he moved away, the other one might get the darshan of the Lord. Ten or fifteen days passed in this manner. Their tapas became the talk of the whole village.

The Lord in the temple did not move. Parvati could not bear to see the severe tapas of the devotees. Her soft heart melted. She asked her Lord, “Don’t you see how they are doing severe austerities? How is it that you have not yet pitied them?” Shiva smiled and said that both of them were dishonest and they would not benefit even if boons were given to them. Parvati could not believe this. “How can that be? Without true devotion, can one continue such severe penance? I think you have become stone-hearted, not to be moved by their plight. Please grant them darshan and boons.”

Pestered by Parvati, Lord Shiva agreed. But he warned her that no good would come of it. He went straight to Sankaran, who had started the tapas first. He stood in front of him and called out, "Sankaran, open your eyes. I am the Lord come to grant you your boon." Sankaran opened his eyes and got up hurriedly to prostrate before the Lord. The Lord said, "Ask for a boon."

Sankaran said, "O Lord, I am a mere mortal, and I don't know much. Please clarify one point for me. Then I shall ask for my boon." The Lord nodded. Sankaran folded his hands and said, "Did you give darshan to Raman, Lord?" The Lord said, "Not yet."

Then Sankaran thought for a moment and said, "Lord, since you are going to give a boon to him also, please let me ask only one thing. Please give me double of what you give him."

Shiva smiled inwardly. He knew that they both wanted to destroy each other. He said, "Tathastu" and moved to the other side, where Raman was sitting.

He stood in front of Raman and said, "Raman, open your eyes. I am the Lord come to give you a boon."

Raman opened his eyes and saw the Lord. He hurriedly got up, prostrated and asked, "O Lord, I am very happy that you have come. Please tell me. Did you go to him?" Lord Shiva knew whom he meant. He nodded. Raman eagerly asked, "What did he ask from you, Lord?"

Lord Shiva said, "He wanted double of what you get from me. I said 'yes' to him."

Raman's eyes glittered with hatred. He would teach that rascal a lesson. Somehow or the other he must make him suffer. But what should he ask from the Lord ?

He thought deeply for some time. Then he folded his hands and said, "Lord, please make me blind in one eye." The Lord smiled. How foolish these men were! "Tathastu." Granting the boon, the Lord disappeared.

Raman became blind in one eye and Sankaran became blind in both eyes. Their boons became the talk of the village for years to come. People often get golden opportunities in life. But sometimes they ruin themselves by wanting the wrong things.

Chattambi Swamigal

Chattambi Swamigal was a scholar-sage of Kerala with superhuman powers. He rarely exhibited his powers but sometimes they showed themselves unexpectedly.

Once, when he was the guest of a magistrate, a new lace cloth was used for covering something in his room. By morning it was full of holes, for the rats had been at it. Naturally, the magistrate was very annoyed.

Swamiji then conducted a trial of the rats, just as a magistrate would in court.

He called out to the rats, “Come on children, all of you gather here!” A large number of rats gathered in his presence. He picked up the spoiled lace cloth in his hand and showed it to them. “Tell me, who has done this?” One of the tiny rats came forward and nodded its head, indicating that it was the guilty one. Then Swamigal asked the magistrate to give the rats a banana each. When they had eaten the

bananas, he told them not to repeat the mistake and sent them away.

After that day, even while Swamigal slept, his things would be safe and no one could take them unless he himself gave them away.

Once, Swamiji was in Parur where he stayed in the Patippura of his host's house. Shortly before the visit, the host brought a clock from Bombay (now Mumbai) which, in those days, was a rarity. The clock was in the room where Swamiji stayed for the night. As Swamiji always slept with the doors and windows open, the host was afraid that the clock might be stolen by someone at night. So he went into Swamiji's room before he turned in for the night, to remove the clock and keep it inside. But Swamiji assured him that no one could take it away without his knowledge. It would be safe.

The host went back, leaving the clock there, but he wanted to test the truth of Swamiji's words that all things would be safe even while he slept. So he got up at night and stealthily entered the room where Swamiji was sleeping. He tiptoed to the clock and stretched his hand out to take it away. But the moment he did so, something like an electric shock ran through his hand and he was rooted to the spot, as if paralysed, his hand stuck to the clock. Try as he might, he could neither walk away nor let go of the clock. He stood there for hours, bound by an unseen power till Swamiji woke up in the morning. Seeing his host with his hand on the clock he smiled and said, "You need not have doubted my word. Now you can leave." As he said these words, his host's hand came away from the clock and he was able to move again.

The Heart in the Tree

Once upon a time a monkey lived on the branches of a roseapple tree, which grew on the banks of a big river. The monkey was a great devotee of Sri Rama and prayed to Him constantly.

As the monkey jumped up and down the branches of the tree, swinging to and fro, he sang his favourite song—

Sri Ram Jaya Ram Jaya Jaya Ram

Repeating the same song over and over, the monkey would eat the roseapples. Singing it, he would rise in the morning and singing it he would go to bed at night.

One day, while he was singing and swinging as usual, some ripe fruit fell from the tree into the river below. A crocodile happened to be in the waters under the tree. As the fruits fell, the crocodile, out of curiosity, ate one, then another and yet another. He liked the taste of the roseapple very much. Lifting his head to see from where the fruits were falling, he saw the

monkey and heard his song. The crocodile said, "Will you be my friend? I like both your song and the fruit that falls from your tree."

The monkey being kind and good-natured, immediately accepted the crocodile as his friend.

As time went by the two friends began to spend more and more time with each other. Gradually, the crocodile came to spend the whole day with the monkey and returned home late at night.

This meant that he neglected his home and his wife. Naturally, the crocodile's wife grew angry and jealous of the unknown monkey with whom her husband spent all his time. Any request, any programme to spend the day together, every effort on the part of the wife to keep her husband at home for some time would be in vain. Mr. Crocodile would put her off, saying, "We will see some other time. I'm in a hurry now. My friend will be waiting for me!" And he would rush off, without hearing a word his wife said.

Mrs. Crocodile was sure that as long as the monkey lived, she would not have her husband to herself. But how could she get rid of the monkey? She schemed and planned and at last cooked up a plot to kill the monkey.

When the husband came home late that night after spending the whole day with the monkey, he found his wife in bed, moaning and groaning, and his dinner not cooked. Anxiously, he went to her and, embracing her lovingly, enquired what was wrong. Heaving a sigh and shedding tears, she groaned, "Headache. A headache so severe and painful, I don't think I shall survive." Thoroughly alarmed now, the husband put his fingers to his wife's lips, and said, "Don't speak inauspicious words, my dear. Of course you will get well. Whoever heard of a crocodile dying of a headache? I will get the doctor right away."

"No, that isn't necessary," moaned the wife, "I have visited him. He doesn't have the medicine but he said, that I would be cured in a flash if I get the medicine he has prescribed. But how to get it?" Mrs. Crocodile groaned again, holding her head in both her hands.

"That should not be a problem, my dear. Am I so useless that I cannot get medicine for you when you are in such pain? Tell me what it is. I shall get it even if it has to be brought from the depths of the oceans."

"You don't have to go that far. It is easy to get if you love me enough," she said.

"How can you doubt my love for you, my dear! Tell me what it is. I shall get it for you immediately."

Mrs. Crocodile laughed inwardly, for her plan was working. Groaning once again she said, "The doctor said that I should apply the paste of a monkey's heart after grinding it thoroughly."

Mr. Crocodile was shocked. A monkey's heart! Of all things, why had he prescribed a monkey's heart ? His best friend's! He could not think coherently. To escape the situation, he muttered, "But how can I get my friend's heart? He lives up on a tree. I cannot climb the tree."

Mrs. Crocodile, with an assumed seriousness and show of pain replied, "No, no, how can I expect you to attempt the impossible? But you can do one thing. Invite him to our house for lunch today. Carry him here on your back . I shall do the rest."

Mr. Crocodile was crestfallen. He did not like the idea of betraying his friend at all. He tried to make excuses. Seeing these signs of weakening, Mrs. Crocodile moaned again. The husband quickly assured her that he would surely get his friend the next day.

The next morning, a loud moan from Mrs. Crocodile awakened her husband, reminding him of his unpleasant duty for the day. He hurriedly washed his face and rushed to the tree, the sighs of his wife ringing in his ears.

Worried, but outwardly calm, he came to the tree and greeted his friend with enthusiasm. The monkey sang out his prayer and the crocodile also joined in. The crocodile said, "Friend, today I have come with an invitation

for you from my wife. She has been asking me to invite you for lunch one of these days. Yesterday she was quite angry with me, because I have been eating all your roseapples and taking some for her too, but so far we haven't given you anything in return. So today, she is preparing lunch for you. Come, let's go."

The monkey was happy at the invitation, but he said, "How can I come to your place? You know I can't swim."

"Yes, yes I know, my friend. Jump on to my back, I will carry you there." The monkey happily jumped on to the crocodile's back, and the crocodile turned and swam towards his home. It had been easy to fool his trusting friend. Now he only had to carry the monkey home and his wife would do the rest. He shuddered at the thought. What a sin he was committing! He was carrying his innocent, trusting friend to his death. The monkey had always been a loving and considerate friend and fed him with fruit and taught him devotional songs, and he was repaying him with treachery!

This thought brought tears to his eyes, and they rolled down his cheeks. The monkey was taken aback and asked in concern, "Why are you sad? This is a happy occasion. Why are you crying?"

The crocodile shed a few more tears and replied, "My friend, forgive me for deceiving you. But I am helpless. My wife has a terrible headache and the paste of a monkey's heart is the only medicine. That's why I'm taking you home."

The poor monkey! They were in the middle of the river now and there was no escape. Was he to die at the hands of an ungrateful friend? Then the monkey thought of his Sri Rama, the helper of the helpless and the strength of the weak. Why should he be afraid? He closed his eyes and fervently chanted his favourite song—

"*Sri Ram Jaya Ram Jaya Jaya Ram.*"

Tremendous strength came from within with this prayer and the monkey felt calmer. A

way out of the predicament suggested itself to him, by the Lord's grace.

He laughed gaily and said, "You're such a fool, my friend! Why didn't you mention this to me before we started from the tree? Now all your efforts are in vain."

"Why so?" asked the crocodile, surprised to see his friend so cheery in such a tight spot.

The monkey laughed again and replied, "I do not have my heart with me now. You know how afraid I am of the water. Fearing it might get wet, I hung it on the branches of the tree before I jumped on to your back. Now you are carrying me to your place, but what is the use?"

The crocodile had a big body but no brain. He did not see through the monkey's cunning. Glumly, he asked, "What should we do now?" The monkey said, "Let's return to the tree quickly so that I can jump up and throw my heart down to you. The sooner the better, otherwise your wife will continue to suffer."

The crocodile was happy at such an easy solution, and swiftly swam back. In no time they were under the tree. The monkey jumped up in one swing and was safely back on the top of the tree. The foolish crocodile waited under the tree, expecting the monkey to throw his heart down to him. After a long time, he raised his head and cried out, "Friend, won't you throw your heart down? I am waiting."

The monkey laughed scornfully and shouted, "Go away, you false friend! Don't show your face here any more. My heart is within me safely, beyond your reach. God has saved me."

The monkey went on singing the song of the Lord, while the foolish crocodile sadly returned to his wife.

The Silly Fly

Long, long ago a fly lived in a small house of her own. One day she was cleaning her house when she suddenly forgot her own name. However much she racked her little brain, she could not remember who she was.

"Dear me!" she thought, "How will I get along without knowing who I am? Let me see if the granny next door remembers my name." She flew to the old woman who was her neighbour and eagerly asked. "Granny, granny, please tell me, do you remember who I am?" The old woman puckered up her face, trying to remember her name but she could not. She shook her head and said, "I cannot say, for the life of me. I have become too old. You can ask my son in the courtyard. He might know what your name is."

The fly flew to the courtyard where the old woman's son was chopping wood. She settled upon a wall nearby and sweetly asked, "O granny, granny, granny's son, do you remember who I am?" The young man stopped his work and looked at the fly. He also shook his head. "I am too busy to remember things like this. Sometimes I forget my own name. How can I remember yours?"

The fly felt miserable. The granny's son felt sorry for her and said, "Don't be sad. Ask the

axe in my hand. Perhaps it remembers your name." The fly's face brightened. She went near the axe and asked anxiously, "O granny, granny, granny's son, O axe in the hand of the granny's son, do you remember who I am?"

The axe mumbled feebly, "Look here, dear, whatever your name is. From early morning this man is swinging me up and down, hitting me against the hard dry wood. He has not given me a moment's rest. My head is reeling. How can I think and remember your name?" The fly was really worried now. "If nobody knows who I am, then I am completely lost." Looking at the worried fly, the axe said kindly, "Don't feel so miserable. I cannot remember because I am too tired. Others may remember you. Ask this wood on the ground. Since morning it has been lying comfortably. It may remember you."

The fly went near the wood and sitting upon the ground, she said softly, "O granny, granny, granny's son, the axe in the hand of the granny's son, O wood being cut by the axe, do you remember who I am? The wood groaned, "From the morning I have been mercilessly cut into pieces, bit by bit. Here I lie, bleeding and dying. How can I remember who you are? See, there is my mother, the tree. She may remember who you are." Even while it spoke, it gasped and cracked as the axe rose heavily in the air and hit it hard. The fly rose up in alarm lest the axe fall upon her too. She flew towards the tree and settled upon a branch.

"O granny, granny, granny's son, the axe in the hand of the granny's son, the wood that is cut by the axe, O tree, mother of the wood being cut, can you tell me who I am? The tree sighed deeply. Shedding tears she said, "Is this the time to crack jokes with me? My children are being cut to pieces right in front of my eyes and you ask me silly questions. If you really don't know who you are, ask the mare who is tied to my trunk. Don't trouble me with your problems."

The fly felt hurt. "I asked you only one little thing. No need to grumble," she said and flew to the mare. "O granny, granny, granny's son, the axe in the hand of granny's son, the wood that is cut by the axe, mother of the wood that is cut, O mare that is tied to the tree, can you tell

me who I am?" The mare moaned in pain. "Look, my dear. I am in great pain, and about to deliver a baby. I have to move a bit to have an easy delivery but they keep me tied up. How can I remember your name? Ask the baby in my womb. He may know who you are."

The fly sighed. How difficult it is to know oneself. She flew near the womb of the mare and whispered, "O unborn baby of the mare in pain, can you tell me who I am?"

The baby from within roared with laughter, "Ha! Ha! Ha! Ho! Ho! Ho! How silly you are! You are just a common house-fly." The fly jumped up in glee, "Ho! Ho! Ho! Ho! Housefly is my name. Now I remember who I am. I am a housefly! A housefly am I!"

Silly, silly housefly! How silly she was! She knew her neighbour and the neighbour's son; she knew the axe and the wood and the tree; she knew the mare and the baby of the mare; she knew everyone except her own self!

The Ant and the Baby

Once upon a time there was a king who had seven sons. One day they all went fishing and caught seven fishes. They brought them all home and dried them in the sun. Six fish dried but the seventh one did not. The seventh prince asked the fish, "O fish, why is it that you alone have not dried up?" The fish replied, "How can I dry when this big bush stands in the way of the sun and blocks its rays?"

The prince asked the bush, "Hey bush, why do you stand in the way of the sun? My fish has remained wet." The bush replied, "How can I move away from the sun by myself unless the horse eats my leaves?"

The prince went to the horse and asked, "O horse, why did you not eat the bush and trim its leaves? My fish is still wet."

The horse replied, "My dear prince, how can I go to the bush by myself when I am tied in this shed? The groom didn't take me out today."

The prince went to the groom and asked, "My man, why did you not take the horse out from the shed today? The horse didn't eat the bush, the bush got in the way of the sun and my fish didn't dry." The groom said, "Sir, how could I take the horse out when I was starving for want of food? Today my mother didn't give me my food."

The prince went to the groom's mother and asked, "O woman, why didn't you give your son food today? He didn't take the horse out. The horse didn't eat the bush. The bush stood in the way of the sun. My fish is still wet." The mother replied, "O Prince, how could I cook the food when the baby was weeping non-stop? I was busy consoling her and had no time to cook the food."

The prince went to the baby and asked, "Silly baby, why did you weep on and on ? Your mother was busy consoling you and didn't cook the food. The groom did not take the horse out. The horse didn't eat the bush. The bush stood in the way of the sun. My fish didn't dry." The baby replied, "I was weeping because I was bitten by the ant!"

The prince went to the ant and asked, "O ant, why did you bite the baby? The baby kept on weeping. The mother was busy consoling her. She could not cook the food. The groom didn't take the horse out. The horse didn't eat the bush. The bush stood in the way of the sun. My fish didn't dry." The ant replied, "I bit the baby because she poked her finger into my anthill!"

Had the baby not put her finger into the anthill, the ant wouldn't have bitten it! The baby wouldn't have wept; the mother wouldn't have failed to cook the food; the groom wouldn't have starved; the horse wouldn't have remained in the shed; the bush wouldn't have remained in the way and the fish wouldn't have remained wet!

Ambarisha

King Ambarisha was a great devotee of Lord Vishnu. He used to observe the *Ekadashi vrata* by observing a fast the whole day and having a meal the next day before forenoon, as enjoined by the Shastras. Throughout his life he observed the *Ekadashi* and became very, very dear to God.

Once, Sage Durvasa came as his guest on *Dwadashi*, that is, the day after *Ekadashi*. Ambarisha received the sage with great reverence and made arrangements for his stay along with his disciples. The sage then told Ambarisha that he would go for his bath and meditation and return by lunch-time. Ambarisha got

the food ready in time for the guests and awaited their return. For some reason the sage delayed his arrival and it was getting late for the *Dwadashi Parana*. According to the rules, a devotee who observed the *Ekadashi* fast was required to eat before noon. But how could one eat before the guest was fed? It was approaching noon, still there was no sign of the guest. The king was in anguish because his fast would go waste if he didn't eat before noon. And if he did, that would be an insult to the invited guest. What a dilemma!

Eager to pacify their king, his ministers suggested that the *Ekadashi vrata* could be completed if he just sipped water and did not eat a full meal. Satisfied that it was so, Ambarisha took water in his palm, offered it to God and sipped it in token of having broken the fast.

Soon after, Durvasa returned, burning with uncontrollable rage. He was furious with Ambarisha for having broken his fast without first feeding his guest. The king's ministers hastened to explain to him that Ambarisha had just sipped water for the sake of the Shastra and that he had not eaten anything. But Durvasa was in no mood to listen. In great wrath, he created an evil Shakti to swallow the king. The terrible-looking Shakti rushed towards Ambarisha, to devour him. The womenfolk of the royal family and the ministers cried out in horror as the fearful Shakti rushed towards Ambarisha, but were helpless to prevent it. Ambarisha stood still, unperturbed and unafraid. He knew that the Lord alone was his refuge. If it was His will that he should perish at the hands of the evil-looking Shakti, then so be it, he thought. He closed his eyes and went on praying to Sri Maha Vishnu with great devotion, forgetting about the impending danger.

How could the kind Lord ever forget His devotee? Sri Maha Vishnu sent his Sudarshana Chakra whirling round to destroy the Shakti and also the egoistic sage who wanted to kill His devotee. The Sudarshana Chakra sent out flashes of lightning and thunder and destroyed the Shakti in no time. Then it turned towards Durvasa to punish him. Durvasa's heart

thumped in fright. He ran for his life, but the Sudarshana Chakra pursued him wherever he went.

There was no escape from it. Durvasa ran to heaven, seeking Indra's help in overcoming the Chakra. But Indra said that he was powerless to counteract Vishnu's Chakra. In despair, Durvasa ran to Kailasha and Satyaloka but both Shiva and Brahma declared that they had no power to pacify the Vishnu Chakra. Now

Durvasa had nowhere to turn to. He ran to Vaikuntha to take refuge in Lord Vishnu Himself. Lord Vishnu looked at Durvasa and turned His head away from him. Durvasa prayed humbly, "Lord of mercy, please pardon me for trying to hurt your devotee. I shall not repeat the mistake. Please recall Your Chakra and relieve me of this great terror."

The Lord spoke softly, "O Sage, if you had harmed Me I could have pardoned you easily. But if you dare to injure My devotees, how can I tolerate it? The Chakra rose by itself from my hands for the protection of My devotee. Now it is not possible even for Me to call it back before it has finished its work. If you want to be saved, there is only one way. Go to him whom you wished to harm without any justification, and beg his pardon. If he forgives you, then the Chakra might be pacified."

Durvasa was dejected. Should he go back to Ambarisha and seek his help? After having wished his destruction, how could he face him? But he had no alternative. Whirling and whistling menacingly, the Chakra was pursuing him and if he remained there any longer, it would cut him to pieces. He ran like a madman, burning with shame and repentance, back to Ambarisha and fell at his feet, "Forgive me, dear devotee of the Lord, forgive me!" Ambarisha looked at him with pity and love and embraced him. He assured the sage that the Chakra would not hurt him. Then the king turned towards the Vishnu Chakra, which was

approaching them fast. He folded his hands with great devotion and prayed to the Chakra. "O Sudarshana, please be pacified. Your name means, 'good vision'. Please discard this fierce appearance of yours. The sage repents what he did in ignorance. I am not angry with him, nor have I been hurt by him. By his action I got a chance to see you. So he is really my benefactor. Please cool down and return to the Lord."

As Ambarisha prayed, the Chakra gradually calmed down and started giving out cool light rays. Ambarisha and Durvasa bowed to the Chakra, which returned to Vaikuntha to adorn the hand of the Lord once again.

Suitably humbled, Durvasa expressed his gratitude to Ambarisha and returned to his ashram.

Gajendra Moksha

Long, long ago, before the dawn of civilisation, India was full of thick forests. In one of these forests lived an elephant king, Gajendra, who had a thousand wives. He lived with them happily, and his wives in turn loved and obeyed him without question.

One day, Gajendra went for a walk, accompanied by all his wives. It was a summer evening and a cool breeze was blowing. Playfully breaking off the green branches of the trees and munching the leaves, they wandered for a long time and covered quite a distance. Then, in the midst of a thick clump of trees, they came across a huge lake of crystal clear water, full of lotuses. The elephant king was drawn towards the lake, which looked so inviting. He entered the lake along with his wives. They filled their trunks with water and sprayed it on one another playfully. When they lifted their trunks up and blew out the water, it formed a fountain and touched the sky. Thus they played for many hours.

It was getting late and they had to return home. One by one, they started coming out of the lake. The last one to come out was Gajendra himself. As he was doing so, a crocodile shot up from under the water and caught hold of his foot.

Gajendra jerked his leg. The crocodile was a little shaken but did not let go. Gajendra tried

again and again to pull his leg free, but to no avail. Now a fight ensued. Gajendra pulled the crocodile towards the banks while the crocodile pulled the elephant towards the centre of the lake. Both being equally powerful, neither could win. Each succeeded alternately, but only partially, thus neither of them was free.

The fight continued for many years. Still neither gave up. The poor wives of Gajendra

stood helplessly on the banks, hoping that their husband would soon become victorious, but in vain. The crocodile was in his own element, gaining strength day by day while Gajendra, away from his home, got weaker and weaker, until one day he knew that he could not fight any more. What was he to do now? His strength was ebbing away and so was his courage. He realized that God alone could be his protector.

He stopped fighting and lifting up his trunk, cried out in despair, "O Lord of the Universe, who has created us all, protect me and save me from the clutches of this terrible crocodile. Sages say that You cannot be seen except with the inner eye. Wise men say that You are the shelter of the shelterless, the wealth of the poor, and the strength of the weak. I am helpless and weak. I have lost all hope and faith in my own strength. Please come and rescue me from this terrible enemy. I have none but You as my refuge."

The cry from his heart went straight to Lord Vishnu, who was in Vaikuntha playing a game with Lakshmi. While playing, He had tied the end of Lakshmi's saree to His own dhoti. When he heard the cry of Gajendra who was in great distress, He rose in a hurry, forgetting everyone. Like a mother who rushes to the side of her baby when it cries out, Sri Maha Vishnu ran out to the elephant king. Poor Lakshmi, whose saree was tied to His dhoti, also had to run along with Him! When the Lord ran out, Garuda, His Vahana and Sudarshana, His Chakra, knew that they would be needed. So they ran behind Him and were followed by all the denizens of Vaikuntha. Thus a great procession came out in the sky in answer to Gajendra's cry for help! Within a few minutes, the Lord, along with His retinue was in the forest. He took his Chakra in hand and sent it flying to cut off the head of the crocodile.

The Lord blessed Gajendra, who praised Him in several hymns. Thereafter, the elephant king lived happily with his wives, continuously remembering the Lord and singing His glories.

The Truthful Cow

Once a cow was grazing in the forest near a village. Usually she grazed on the fringe of the forest, but that day she forgot herself and went deeper into the forest. As she was busy eating the grass, she suddenly heard a terrifying roar. Almost immediately, a lion was upon her, raising his paw to tear her flesh.

The cow lost all hope of survival.

At that moment she remembered the innocent face of her young calf, who would be eagerly waiting for her return. If she were to die now and not return home, who would feed her child? The mother cow could not bear the

thought of her calf starving, with no one to look after it.

If only she could go home once, she could make some arrangement for her calf. Would the lion allow her to go home and return, before he killed her?

Shedding tears, the cow looked piteously at the lion and said, "Sir, I am in your hands and cannot escape. Please allow me one final wish before you kill me." The lion was surprised. Never before had any animal talked to him like this. What did the cow want? "What do you wish to say?" asked the lion, his raised paw still in mid-air.

The cow said, "Sir, I have a young calf at home who is barely seven days old. This is the usual time for me to return home and feed my child. If you kill me right now, my baby will not know what has happened to me. It will be eagerly waiting for my return. It has no one to look after him. If you show me mercy and permit me to go home for a while, I shall feed it for the last time and make some arrangements for its future and quickly return to you. Please give me some time."

The lion laughed uproariously, "Do you expect me to believe you? Once you are allowed to go home, will you be foolish enough to return to become my food? A being in danger makes all sorts of promises. The moment the danger has passed, it conveniently forgets all its promises. I would be a fool if I listened to you."

"No, Sir, believe me. Throughout my life I have never uttered a lie. Now, face-to-face with death, would I lie? I solemnly promise you that I will return within an hour to become your food. Please show some consideration for a mother's heart."

The cow's piteous look melted even the cruel heart of the lion. He said, "I know that I am a fool to believe you. But let me see if you are really truthful. I will give you one hour. Go home and return. I will wait for you."

The cow was besides herself with joy. She thanked the lion and ran home. As expected, her calf was eagerly waiting for her. The moment it saw her, it came rushing forward for its milk. The cow stood still, licking the calf and shedding tears. After the calf had finished drinking the milk, she gently broke the news that she was to die and become the lion's food. The calf clung to her and wept bitterly. It even suggested that she should not go back to the lion but remain safely at home. But the mother cow told the young baby that to tell a lie was worse than death. One should always be truthful, come what may. She advised the calf to always live truthfully and righteously. She entrusted it to the care of another cow, licked the calf once more and returned to the forest.

Exactly one hour had passed by then and the lion was wondering whether the cow would really return. Were there still truthful people left in the world? As he was debating this within himself, he saw the cow hurrying towards him. The lion could hardly believe his eyes. But no, his eyes were not deceiving him. There was the cow, in flesh and blood, standing before him. She expressed her gratitude for being allowed to go home. She said, "Sir, by your grace I was able to feed my baby for the last time, and give him good advice as to how he should live in future. Thank you very much. I am now ready. Please eat me."

At this, even the lion's hard heart melted. Shedding tears of remorse, he said, "Mother, go home to your child and live happily. Your very honesty and love of truth have moved my heart. I cannot kill you."

Kannappa

The famous pilgrimage centre of Sri Kalahasti is near Tirupati in Andhra Pradesh. Originally, the whole area was covered with forests and hardly anyone knew about the existence of a Linga there. Only one devout Brahmin used to go there once a fortnight to worship the Lord.

One day, a tribal boy happened to pass through that part of the forest while hunting in the jungle. The moment he saw the Linga, he was intensely attracted to it. The boy's name was Kannappa. From that day onwards he started visiting the place, spending time with the Lord and innocently prattling to him. Every day he hunted animals and brought their meat for the Lord to eat. He would offer it with love and the Lord would eat it. Then he would return the next day for the same purpose. It struck him one day that the Lord would need a bath too. There was water in the nearby river but how to get it here? So when he had prepared the meat of the animals, he started putting it in two leaf plates. Carrying them in both his hands, he would go to the river and fill up his mouth with water and come to the Linga.

There he would puff the water out of his mouth and wash the Linga. Then he would

offer the meat that he had brought. He derived great pleasure out of this worship.

After a fortnight, the Brahmin from the village came to do his regular puja. He was an educated man and knew the method of puja according to the Shastras. When he saw the dried-up meat offerings and the Linga full of the spit of some unknown forester, he shuddered with revulsion. He could not leave the Lord in such a condition. He cleaned the whole place and brought plenty of water from the river and washed the Linga again and again. Then he chanted the purifactory mantras and concluded his puja for the day. He hoped that such a thing would not happen again.

But his hope was in vain. Kannappa was so devoted to the Lord that he could not remain without doing his puja to the Lord for even a single day. Thus when the Brahmin returned after another fortnight, he was pained to see the polluted condition of the Lord. Again he patiently cleaned up the whole mess, did his puja and went back. Thus it happened a number of times. The Brahmin was in tears to see this unholy pollution every time he came to worship. Weeping bitterly at the dirty condition of the Lord, he prayed, "O Lord, you are the purest of all. You are the Holy of holies. Why do you allow this impurity to be done to you? You are the protector of the whole world. Please protect Yourself from all this."

When the Brahmin prayed sincerely out of true devotion, the Lord spoke, "Brahmin, do not grieve. The devotee who offers this puja is pure at heart, though he is ignorant of the sacred ways of the Shastras. I am bound to him by his pure love, therefore I accept his puja. It is now time for him to come.

Hide yourself behind the tree and see how devoted he is. Then you will understand why I cannot refuse his offerings."

The Brahmin hid himself behind a tree, from where he could see the Lord and the surrounding area clearly.

After some time, Kannappa came, with his mouth full of water, carrying two leaves containing the meat. He puffed the water from his mouth over the Linga and offered the meat

as usual. But that day the Lord didn't eat it. Kannappa was surprised and begged the Lord, but still the Lord did not oblige.

Kannappa was baffled. Why wasn't the Lord taking His food as usual? As he looked intently, he found that the right eye of the Lord was red and that water was oozing from it. Then Kannappa knew that the Lord's eye was hurting, which is why He did not eat the food. Kannappa ran into the forest and brought all the roots and leaves used to cure eye complaints. He applied them one by one. Instead of getting cured, the eye became worse and blood started streaming from it. Now the boy did not know what to do. So he plucked out his right eye with the sharp end of an arrow and similarly plucked out the sick eye of the Lord. Then he inserted his own eye in the eye socket of the Lord. The eye was now cured.

The happy Kannappa offered the meat and asked the Lord to eat. But then the left eye of the Lord started dripping blood. This time Kannappa did not run about. He plucked out

the left eye of the Lord. Before taking out his own left eye which was the only eye he had now, he lifted his foot with the chappal on, and put it near the Lord's left eye, so that he would know where to put it in the Lord's face. Then he took out the arrow to pluck out his left eye.

At that moment the Lord came out of the Linga and gave Kanappa darshan in His real form, preventing him from plucking out his eye. With a glance the Lord restored Kannappa's right eye. He called the Brahmin from his hiding place. The Brahmin, lost in admiration for the absolute devotion of the boy, came singing the Lord's praises. Thus the Brahmin and the tribal boy both came to be blessed by Lord Shiva. It was not the manner of their worship that brought them the benefit of the Lord's grace, but the devotion behind it.

Action Songs

HONEY BEE

"Honey Bee, Honey Bee, where will you go?
Honey Bee, Honey Bee, what will you do?"

"I will go to the little flower to say hello.
I will kiss the little flower and drink honey sweet."

"Honey Bee, Honey Bee, where will you go?
Honey Bee, Honey Bee, what will you give?"

"I will go to the flower to say hello.
I will kiss the little flower and give her a fruit."

ROSES

Lo! On the mountain the sun has come
One little red rose looked at him.

Lo! On the mountain the sun has come,
Two little roses smiled at him.

Lo! On the mountain the sun has come
Three little roses laughed with him.

Lo! On the mountain the sun has come
Four little roses bloomed into red.

THE CAT IN KAILASH

"Pussy cat, Pussy cat, where did you go?"
"I went to the Silver Mount to see our Lord.
I went to Kailash to see our Gods!"

"Pussy cat, Pussy cat, whom did you see?"
"I saw Lord Shiva and Goddess Parvati.
I saw Lord Ganesh and mewed at His mouse."

"Pussy cat, Pussy cat, what did you do?"
"I put out my paw for the mouse in the Mount.
Very very frightened, I came running back."

HARI OM

Say Hari Om! Hari Om! Hari Om!
Say Hari Om! Hari Om! Hari Om!

It's not at all hard to say Hari Om,
Not at all, not at all, not at all.

Say with a smile, Hari Om! Hari Om!
Part with a smile, Hari Om! Hari Om!

Hari Om! Hari Om! Hari Om!

Dhruva

Scene One

(The palace of the junior queen Suruchi. King Uttanapada is seated on a chair. His second son Uttama, a five - year - old boy is on his lap. Suruchi is weaving a flower garland, standing near a small table.)

Uttanapada: *(embracing his son with great tenderness)* Where have you been since morning, my son? I looked everywhere but could not find you. Why did you not give me the first kiss in the morning?

Uttama: *(kissing him on both cheeks)* Papa, when I got up from bed, I saw a bird on the tree, sitting like this *(crouches in imitation)*. I ran out to catch it.

Uttanapada: *(holding the boy in his arms)* Really! Did you catch it?

Uttama: *(shaking his head)* No, Papa. I just went slowly, like this *(showing how he walked on tiptoe)* without making any sound, but it flew away.

Suruchi: *(smiling)* How could you expect to catch the bird? When you went out, you were shouting and clapping your hands. The bird heard you coming and flew away.

Uttama: Mother, tomorrow I will go chupchaap, chupchaap and catch the bird. *(Both the father and the mother laugh.)*

Dhruva: *(comes running)* Father, Father! See what I have brought for you. *(He is of the same age as Uttama. He has two lotuses in his hand. He approaches his father, gives the flowers to him and tries to sit on his lap along with Uttama.)*

Suruchi: *(Face turning red, she drops the garland on the table and rushes to Dhruva and grabbing his hand drags him roughly away from Uttanapada.)* You silly boy! Who asked you to come here? How dare you sit beside my son?

Dhruva: *(looking hurt)* Mother, I only want to sit on Father's lap.

Suruchi: *(mimicking him)* I want to sit on Father's lap! The great man has come! Who are you to sit on his lap? Get away from here.

Dhruva: *(with tears in his eyes)* Mother, Uttama is sitting on Father's lap. Why can't I? He is my father also.

Suruchi: *(shouting at him in anger)* Yes, yes he is your father. But who is your mother? Uttama is my son. Whose son are you? Had you been

lucky enough, you would have been born to me instead of to Suniti. Only my son can sit on his father's lap. Go and do tapas in the forest and be born as my son in your next life. Then you can sit on your father's lap. Go away. *(She pushes him towards the door.)*

(Dhruva, shedding tears, looks at his father hopefully. Uttanapada remains indifferent. Disappointed, Dhruva leaves the place.)

(Curtain comes down.)

Scene Two

(Senior queen Suniti's palace. Suniti is in front of the deity, doing puja and singing a bhajan in a low voice.)

Dhruva: *(enters, weeping loudly)* Maa... maa...

Suniti: *(Stops the bhajan and hurriedly gets up. She embraces Dhruva, and wipes his tears.)* My son, why are you weeping? Did you fall? Has anyone said anything to you? Did you quarrel with anyone?

Dhruva: *(weeping as if his heart would break, talks amidst sobs)* Mother... Mother...

Suniti: *(anxiously)* Yes, darling. Tell me. Don't be afraid. No one will hurt you. Where did you go? With whom were you talking?

Dhruva: *(still sobbing)* Mother... I took two flowers for Father... Father was sitting... Uttama was on his lap... I went to Father and gave him the flowers... I got on to Father's lap. Then... Maa... *(weeps uncontrollably.)*

Suniti: *(biting her lip)* What happened then, beta ?*(She kisses him affectionately.)*

Dhruva: *(weeping loudly at the memory)* She caught me by my hand and dragged me down... she pushed me near the door... she said that I should go to the forest and do tapas to be born in her womb... she said I am not lucky... That is why I am your son... Why, Mother?

Suniti: *(Struggling in vain to hold back her tears. She embraces her son sadly.)* Yes, my son. You are unfortunate. Otherwise you would not be born to this miserable woman. My poor boy, what can I do? Your father does not love me. He loves Suruchi. That is why she is so proud. *(She weeps forlornly, clasping Dhruva tightly to her heart.)*

Dhruva: *(wipes her tears)* No, Mother, don't cry. I will go to the forest and do tapas. I will ask God that Father may love you and take me on his lap.

Suniti: *(beside herself with grief)* My dear, as long as I alone was neglected and insulted, I could bear it. How can I see you being insulted on my account? Beta, why were you not born to her, like Uttama?

Dhruva: *(embracing her)* Don't cry, Mother. I love you. I wouldn't like to be Suruchi's son. She is hard-hearted. I will go to the forest. Tell me, Mother. Where is the forest? Who is God? Where can I see Him?

Suniti: *(once more clasping the boy to her heart)* Alas! My son. What misfortune has come to you, at this tender age that you think of the forest! *(wipes her tears)* Yes, perhaps that is the best thing to do. God will be your guide! Yes, son. Go to the forest and sincerely pray to the Lord. He alone can remove your distress.

(Both of them get up. Suniti goes in and brings a cloth made of the bark of trees.)

Suniti: *(kneeling in front of Dhruva and removing his ornaments one by one)* Beta, when you do tapas, you should not wear these ornaments and silk robes. You must wear these rough clothes. *(She ties the bark-cloth round his waist like a loin cloth.)*

Dhruva: Where is the forest, Mother?

Suniti: Wait, I will show you. *(She goes in and brings a deer skin, a lota and a stick.)* Take these with you, my son. When you go to the forest, select a place very near the river so that you can have water to drink. Sit under a shady tree, upon the deer-skin, and think of the Lord. Come here, son. *(She takes him near the deity, whom she was worshipping.)* This is the Lord Narayana. He has the lotus, conch, mace and discus in His four hands. He wears yellow clothes, and a Vaijayantimala around His neck, the Kaustubha jewel on his chest. Have you carefully noticed all of them?

Dhruva: *(carefully observing all the features)* Yes, Mother. Should I think of the Lord in this way?

Suniti: Yes. First sit upon the deer-skin like this *(she shows the erect posture.)* Then close your eyes and think of the Lord. If he doesn't come, then stand like this and think of him again. If He fails to come even then, stand on your toe like this and meditate. He will surely give darshan to you one day. *(As she talks, she shows the postures.)*

Dhruva: I understand, Mother. Now show me the way to the forest. I will go there .

Suniti: *(comes to the door along with him and points)* There! That is the path leading to the forest. Next to the forest is the river. Stay near the river. When you feel afraid, pray to the Lord and He will help you. Go, my son. *(She embraces him and bids him farewell with tears in her eyes.)*

Dhruva: I will come back soon, Mother. *(He takes up the skin, lota and stick and goes out.)*

Suniti: *(Sobbing uncontrollably)* Dear God, protect and guide my innocent son.*(She kneels before the deity and prostrutes.)*

(Curtain comes down.)

Scene Three

(Dhruva is walking on the road all alone, carrying the articles his mother has given him. He is almost by the edge of the forest. Narada enters from the opposite direction, playing on his tanpura and singing a bhajan to Narayana.)

Narada: *(stopping in front of Dhruva)* Who are you, my boy? Where are you going all alone? What are those articles in your hand?

Dhruva: *(prostrating to the sage)* I am the son of King Uttanapada, venerable Sir.

Narada: *(feigning surprise)* Really? If you are a prince, why are you in this dress?

Dhruva: Sir, I am going to the forest to do tapas.

Narada: *(smiling)* Tapas? A nice thing to do for a youngster like you. Are you running away from school? Is your mother angry with you? Does she know where you are going?

Dhruva: Yes, Sir, she herself told me to go for tapas. My father does not love me. I shall ask Lord Narayana to make him love my mother and me.

Narada: My child, you are too young to go to the forest and do tapas. I shall come with you and tell your father to love you well. He will listen to me.

Dhruva: No, Sir. I shall not return without seeing the Lord and getting his blessings. I must meet Him.

Narada: What you want is only love, isn't it? Come with me to my ashram. There are many people there. They will love you and look after you well.

Dhruva: No, Sir, I want my father to love me. What is the use of others loving me? I will not go without meeting the Lord.

Narada: Do you know how many fierce animals there are in the forest? If they come rushing at you, where will you hide? Who will look after you? Listen to me, my child, and go back to your parents.

Dhruva: My mother told me, Sir, that God will protect me when I am afraid. I shall pray to Him. I shall not return without meeting the Lord.

Narada: *(smiles approvingly)* Shabash beta, you are quite determined. You will certainly have darshan of the Lord. Come here. I will give you a mantra. Repeat it after me. *(Dhruva approaches him and stands. Narada bends down and gives the mantra thrice, making Dhruva repeat it.)* Say, Om Namo Bhagavate Vasudevaya! Om Namo Bhagavate Vasudevaya! Om Namo Bhagavate Vasudevaya! *(Dhruva repeats after him.)* Now my son, go ahead and do your tapas. Don't be afraid.

(Dhruva prostrates to the sage and goes towards the forest.)

(Curtain comes down.)

Scene Four

(In the forest. Dhruva is sitting on the deer-skin under a tree. He is erect in Padmasana, with eyes closed.).

Dhruva: *(loudly chanting)* Om Namo Bhagavate Vasudevaya! Om Namo Bhagavate Vasudevaya! Om Namo Bhagavate Vasudevaya! *(While chanting, he suddenly opens his eyes.)* Ah, my Lord, at last you have come! *(He looks around and finds it was his delusion.)* Oh! Once again I am deceived. I thought you have come and called me. My mistake again. No, I shall not open my eyes at any cost.

(Curtain falls and rises immediately.)

Dhruva: *(standing now)* Om Namo Bhagavate Vasudevaya! Om Namo Bhagavate Vasudevaya! Om Namo Bhagavate Vasudevaya! *(He stops and listens with closed eyes. Then opens them with a smile.)* Ah, this time you have surely come. *(He looks around and is disappointed. He again closes his eyes and resumes his chanting.)*

(Curtain falls and rises once more.)

Dhruva: *(standing on his right toe)* Om Namo Bhagavate Vasudevaya! Om Namo Bhagavate Vasudevaya! Om Namo Bhagavate Vasudevaya!

(Suddenly Lord Narayana appears in front of Dhruva with four hands, etc. Dhruva continues his meditation with closed eyes.)

Narayana: Dhruva, I am happy with your tapas and have come to give you your boons. Open your eyes and see me. *(Dhruva stops*

chanting ,but he still stands in the same position without opening his eyes.)

Narayana: *(once again)* Dhruva, I am pleased with your tapas and have come to give you your boons. Your tapas is over. Open your eyes and look at me.

Dhruva: *(still remaining as he is, with eyes closed)* Lord, how can I be sure that you have really come and that it is not a delusion this time? Many times I thought that you came and called me. When I opened my eyes, I found no one there. This time also I may be deceived. If

you have really come, show yourself inside me. Then I shall open my eyes.

Narayana: *(laughs)* Alright. See Me inside your mind. *(lifts His hand as if to bless.)*

Dhruva: *(opens his eyes in great joy)* Lord, you have really come. You are exactly like the Lord shown by my mother. How can I speak to you, Lord? I don't know anything!

Narayana: *(stretches out His hand and touches Dhruva with his conch)* Speak, Dhruva.

(Dhruva, getting sudden enlightenment, speaks eloquently.)

Ah, my kindly Lord, the God of my heart,
By Thy grace indeed I find my voice;
O Lord of the disc, lotus and the conch!
The Lord with the fierce mace in the hand
Thou effulgent, Thou resplendent

Thou art the Self! Thou the Supreme!
Thou art full! Thou indeed the world!
Thou verily the beginning and end,
Thou without beginning and end,
Thou within and Thou all-pervading
Thou that art farthest, Thou that art nearest.

Smaller than the smallest and bigger than the biggest!
Thou standeth bearing the whole world in Thee.
Brahma with four heads and Sesha with a thousand tongues are unable to describe Thee.
Who am I to attempt! Blessed am I, blessed indeed! Blessed again and again am I!

Narayana: Dhruva! I am very pleased with you. Go back to your father. Now you will be loved not only by your father but by your stepmother and brother too. Live long, rule the kingdom long. When you complete your earthly life, you will stand in yonder sky as the Dhruva Nakshatra and will illumine the path of thousands.

(The Lord blesses Dhruva as he prostrates before him . Curtain falls. The End.)

Sweetness

Sweet are His lips,

Sweet His face,

Sweet are His eyes,

Sweet His smile,

With His toddling gait,

What a sweetheart is He!

Indeed,

Everything about the sweet Lord

is Sweet alone!

CODE OF CONDUCT FOR THE CHINMAYA MISSION MEMBERS

Chinmaya Mission members should:

- Try to live up to and fulfill the motto as well as the pledge of the Mission.
- Daily spare time for meditation and scriptural study.
- Once a week, on a convenient day offer prayers at a nearby temple with members of their family.
- Discover a life of harmony at home and on no account create any domestic unhappiness.
- Have satsang at home with the children and other family members. Reading of the Ramayana, Mahabharata and Bhagavat Mahapurana in a language familiar to the children would be an important part of the programme.
- Greet other Mission members with 'Hari Om'.
- Inculcate the practice of daily offering pranams to the elders in the house.

THE CHINMAYA MISSION PLEDGE

We stand as one family,
bound to each other with love and respect.

We serve as an army
courageous and disciplined,
ever ready to fight against
all low tendencies and false values,
within and without us.

We live honestly
the noble life of sacrifice and service,
producing more than what we consume,
and giving more than what we take.

We seek the Lord's grace
to keep us on the path of virtue, courage
and wisdom.

May Thy grace and blessings
flow through us to the world around us.

We believe that the service of our country
is the service of the Lord of Lords,
and devotion to the people
is the devotion to the Supreme Self.

We know our responsibilities,
give us the ability and courage
to fulfill them.

Om Tat Sat